DATE DUE

Insects

Library of Congress Number: 77-27130

1   2   3   4   5   6   7   8   9   0   82   81   80   79   78

Printed and bound in the United States of America.

Library of Congress Cataloging in Publication Data

Kirkpatrick, Rena K.
   Look at insects.

   Includes index.
   SUMMARY: Easy-to-read text and illustrations
describe various insects.

   1.   Insects — Juvenile literature. [1.   In-
sects]   I.   Farmer, Andrew.   II.   Title.
QL467.2.W54   595.7   77-27130
ISBN 0-8393-0062-X lib. bdg.

Look At
INSECTS

Words by Rena K. Kirkpatrick
Science Consultant

Pictures by Andrew Farmer

Raintree Childrens Books
Milwaukee • Toronto • Melbourne • London

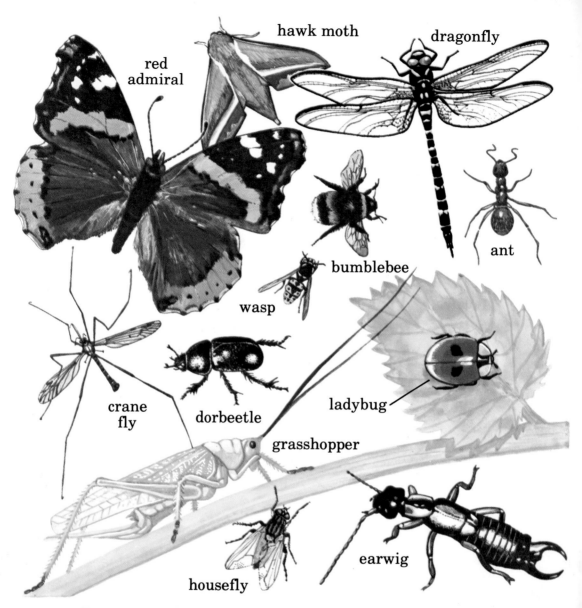

red
admiral

hawk moth

dragonfly

ant

bumblebee

wasp

crane
fly

dorbeetle

ladybug

grasshopper

housefly

earwig

Insects come in many sizes, shapes, and colors. We call some of them "bugs." Not all bugs are insects. How can we identify an insect?

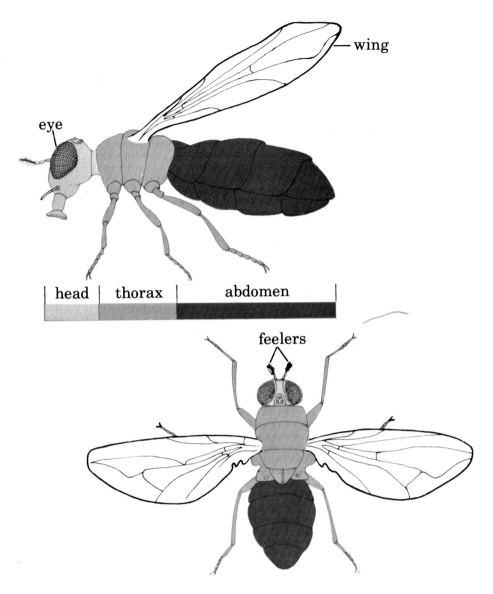

All insects have 3 parts to their bodies. They all have 6 legs. Most insects have 4 wings. Some insects have only 2 wings.

Butterflies

cabbage

red admiral

small
tortoiseshell

buddleia

painted lady

All insects need food, water, and
air. These beautiful butterflies are
insects. They come to the flowers
for food.

eggs

caterpillar

pupa

clear plastic

nasturtium leaves

tape

water

butterfly

There are three stages in the life of a butterfly. The caterpillar stage is first. This stage is sometimes called a larva. The next stage is a pupa. The butterfly comes out of the pupa.

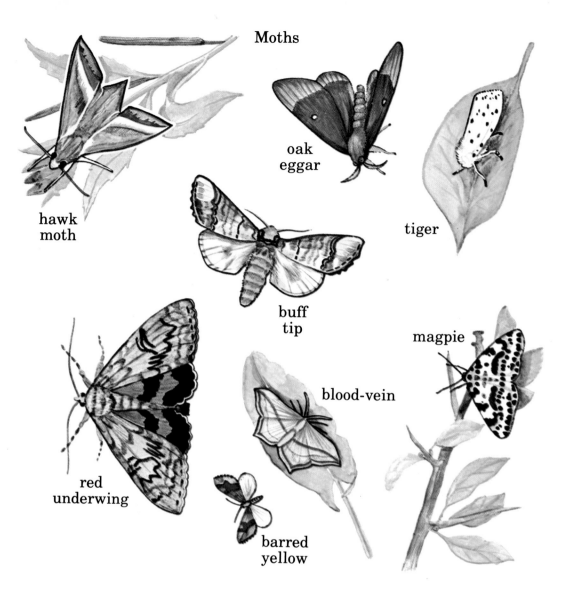

Moths

oak
eggar

hawk
moth

tiger

buff
tip

magpie

blood-vein

red
underwing

barred
yellow

Moths also grow in three stages. Moths are usually seen at night. They fly toward lights. You can see them around your house.

dandelions

cocoon

woolly-bear caterpillar

garden tiger moth

Each different caterpillar makes a different moth or butterfly. You see caterpillars in the spring. They eat dandelion leaves. The pupa stage for this moth is called a cocoon. The moth comes out of the cocoon in the summer.

cinnabar moth
caterpillars

soil

pupa

cinnabar
moth

Some caterpillars go into the soil to change to a pupa. The pupa of the cinnabar moth stays in the soil all summer, fall, and winter. In the spring, the moth comes out.

pupa

glass or plastic jar

pupae

plastic
margarine tub

These children have some soil from
under bushes. They are finding moth
pupae in the soil. After many months
the moths will come out. The jar
over the tub keeps the moths from
flying away.

cuckoo spit

froghopper nymph

A pupa is sometimes called a
nymph. Cuckoo spit hides the nymph
of the hopper insect while it grows.
The cuckoo spit is like the cocoon of
the moth. Hopper insects are also
called spittlebugs.

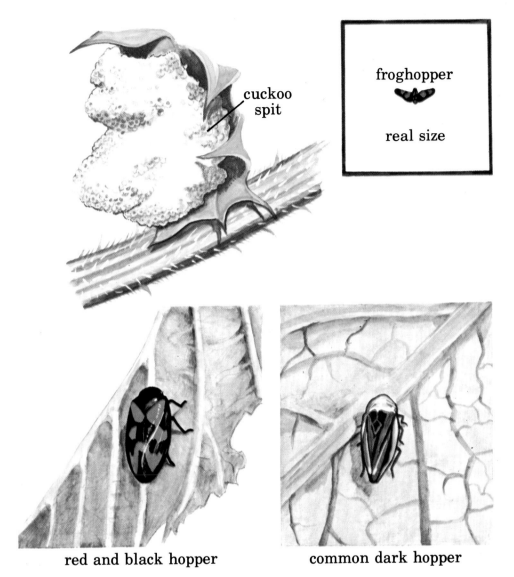

cuckoo spit

froghopper

real size

red and black hopper

common dark hopper

Hopper insects are very small.
They leap like frogs. These insects
suck their food from plants. Look
carefully for them, or they will
hop away.

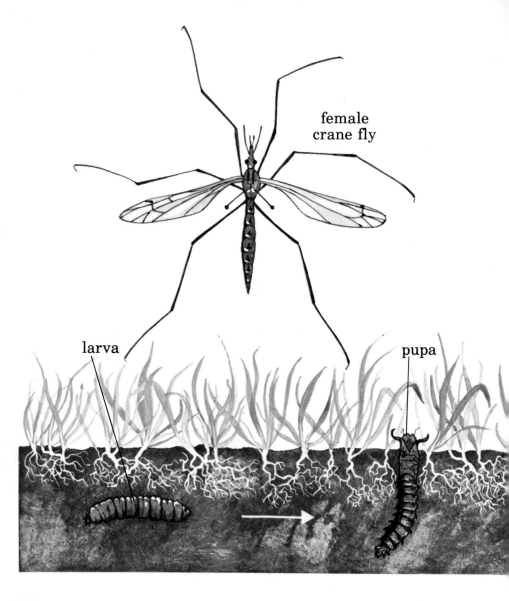

female
crane fly

larva

pupa

The crane fly is an insect with only two wings. The female lays eggs in the grass. The larva hatches from the egg. The larva is called a leather jacket. It goes into the soil and eats grass roots.

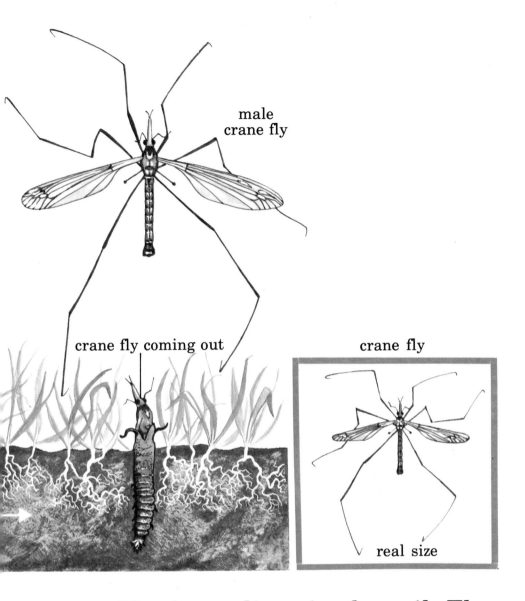

male
crane fly

crane fly coming out

crane fly

real size

The larva lives in the soil. The pupa grows during the winter. In late summer, the crane fly comes out of the pupa. Crane flies look like large mosquitoes. They do not bite like mosquitoes do.

common
7-spot ladybug

10-spot
ladybug

22-spot
ladybug

6-spot
ladybug

2-spot
ladybug

eyed
ladybug

Ladybugs are brightly colored beetles. There are many different kinds. Each kind has a different number of spots. You find them when the weather is warm.

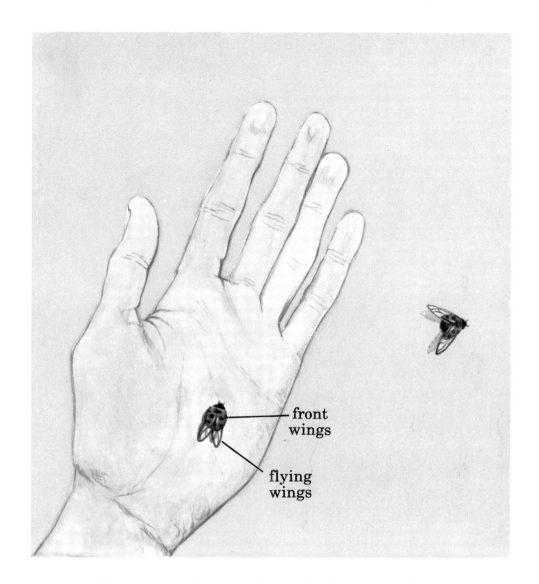

front
wings

flying
wings

Beetles have hard front wings.
Under the front wings are other
wings. These are the flying wings.
Ladybugs do not harm plants. They
eat other insects.

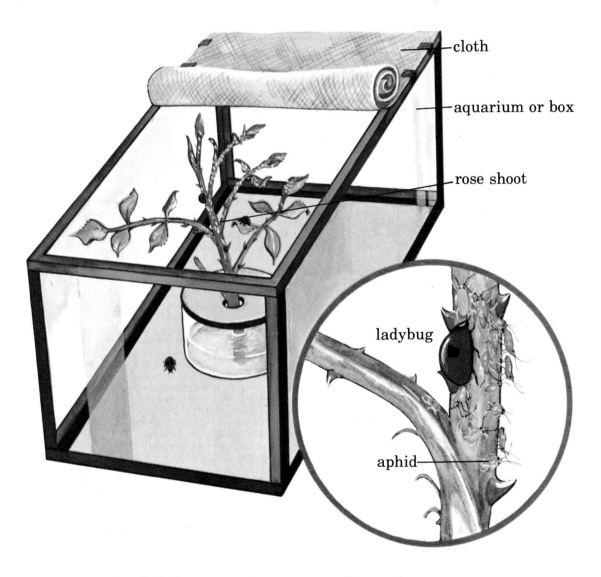

cloth

aquarium or box

rose shoot

ladybug

aphid

Aphids are insects that harm plants. Ladybugs eat aphids. They will help keep your roses healthy. It is easy to keep ladybugs. Feed them aphids.

rose
chafer

cardinal
beetle

two-colored leaf beetle

soldier beetle

All beetles do not have spots. Most
of them are colorful. Make a list of all
the beetles you find.

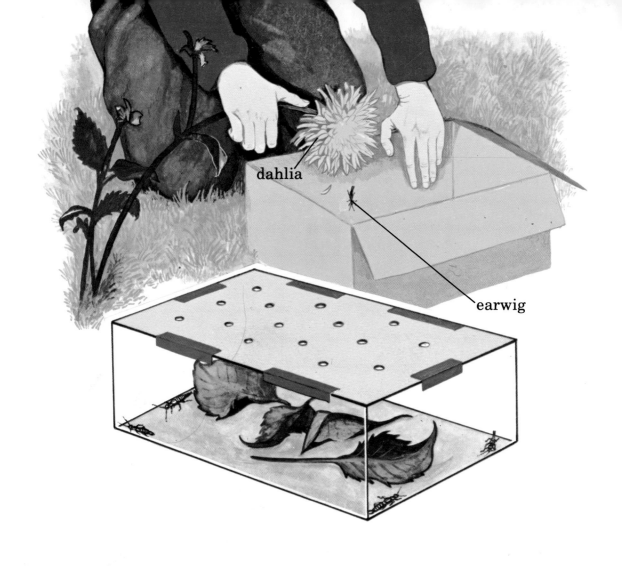

dahlia

earwig

Earwigs are beetles. They are
not colorful. Earwigs live between
flower petals and eat plant leaves.
They like to press themselves into
corners if they are put into a box.
They are trying to hide as they do
in the flowers.

male earwig   female earwig

earwig

real size

The feelers of an earwig have
many joints. They have hard front
wings. They also have small flying
wings, but they never fly. You may
find an earwig by gently shaking a
flower.

21

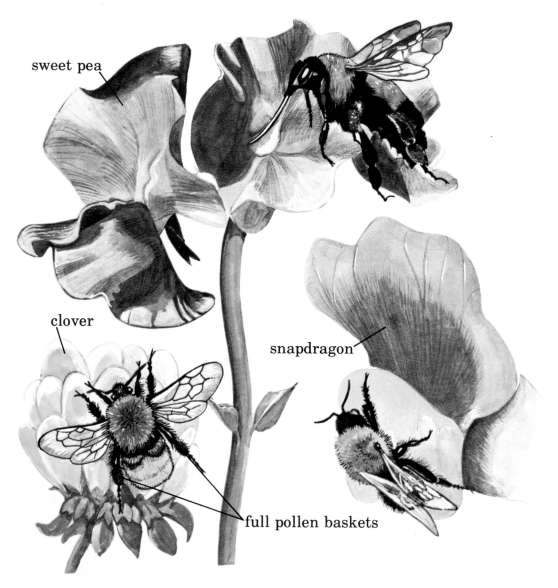

sweet pea

clover

snapdragon

full pollen baskets

Bees are insects too. Bees reach into flowers for nectar. This is food for bees. They carry pollen on their legs from flower to flower.

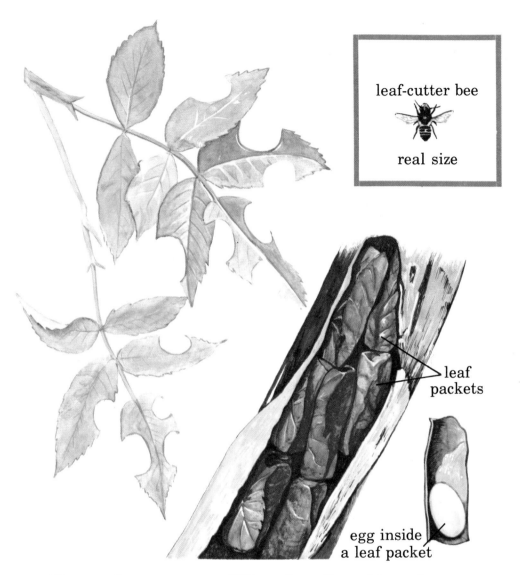

leaf-cutter bee

real size

leaf packets

egg inside a leaf packet

Bees lay eggs. The leaf-cutter bee cuts a piece out of a leaf to wrap around the egg. This hides the egg so it is safe. The bee does not eat the leaf.

Some wasps live in groups. They
build nests. There is a special group
of wasps called workers. Female
and worker wasps sting if you
bother them.

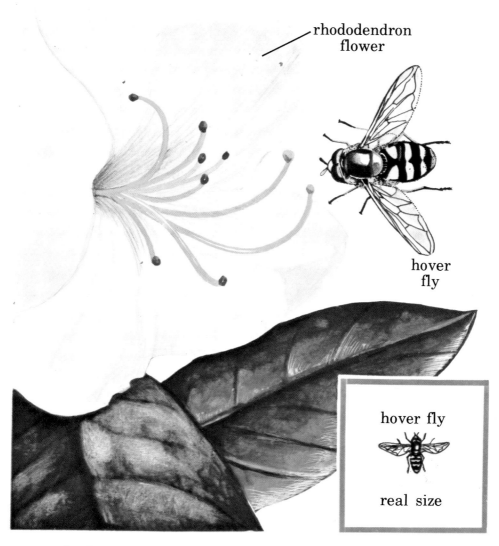

rhododendron
flower

hover
fly

hover fly

real size

A hover fly looks like a wasp. It is not a wasp. It has only two wings. It does not sting. It hovers near flowers. That is where it gets its name. The hover fly eats nectar.

anthill

Many ants live in groups. Some
ants live under the ground. Some live
in an anthill made of twigs and
stems. There is a special group of ants
called workers.

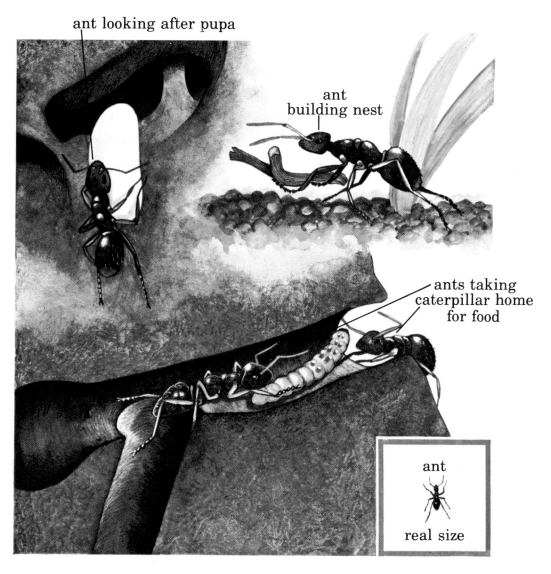

ant looking after pupa

ant building nest

ants taking caterpillar home for food

ant

real size

Worker ants have certain jobs. Some collect food. Some build and take care of the nest. Others guard the nest. Some look after the eggs and pupae of all of the ants.

dragonfly

caddis fly

dragonfly larva

caddis fly larva cases

The caddis fly and the dragonfly are different from other insects. They spend part of their lives in water. The caddis fly larva makes a case for itself. The adult caddis fly comes out of the case.

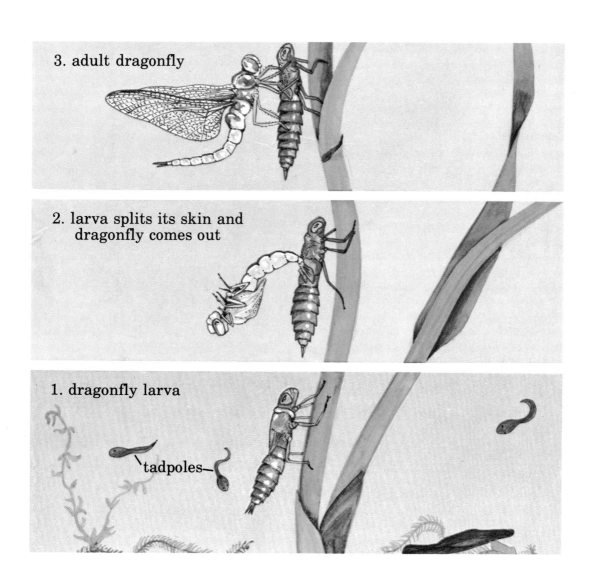

3. adult dragonfly

2. larva splits its skin and
   dragonfly comes out

1. dragonfly larva

tadpoles—

The dragonfly larva eats tadpoles.
When the larva is grown, it crawls up
the stem. The skin splits, and the
adult dragonfly comes out. The
dragonfly has pretty wings. They look
like lace.

What I Know About Insects

Insects have three parts to their bodies.

Insects have six legs.

Most insects have four wings.

Butterflies and moths are insects.

Butterflies and moths have three stages
in their lives.

The three stages are called larva, pupa, and
adult.

Insects with hard front wings are called
beetles.

Ladybugs are helpful insects.

Bees are insects.

Bees carry pollen from one flower to another.

Some wasps live in groups.

Female and worker wasps will sting.

Many ants live in groups.

Worker ants do the work.

The caddis fly and dragonfly live part of
their lives in the water.

Can You Answer These Questions?

1. How many legs do all insects have?

2. What are the three stages in the life of a butterfly?

3. What is the pupa stage of the moth called?

4. How do hopper insects get their food?

5. What do ladybugs eat?

6. Where do earwigs live?

7. How does the leaf-cutter bee hide its eggs?

8. Where do wasps live?

9. What do you call the ants that guard the nests?

10. How is the dragonfly different from other insects?

ANSWERS

1. Six.
2. Larva, pupa, butterfly.
3. Cocoon.
4. They suck food from plants.
5. Insects.
6. Between flower petals.
7. It wraps the eggs with a piece of a leaf.
8. In nests.
9. Workers.
10. It lives part of its life in the water.

31

Words in INSECTS

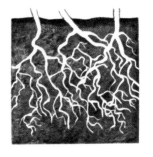